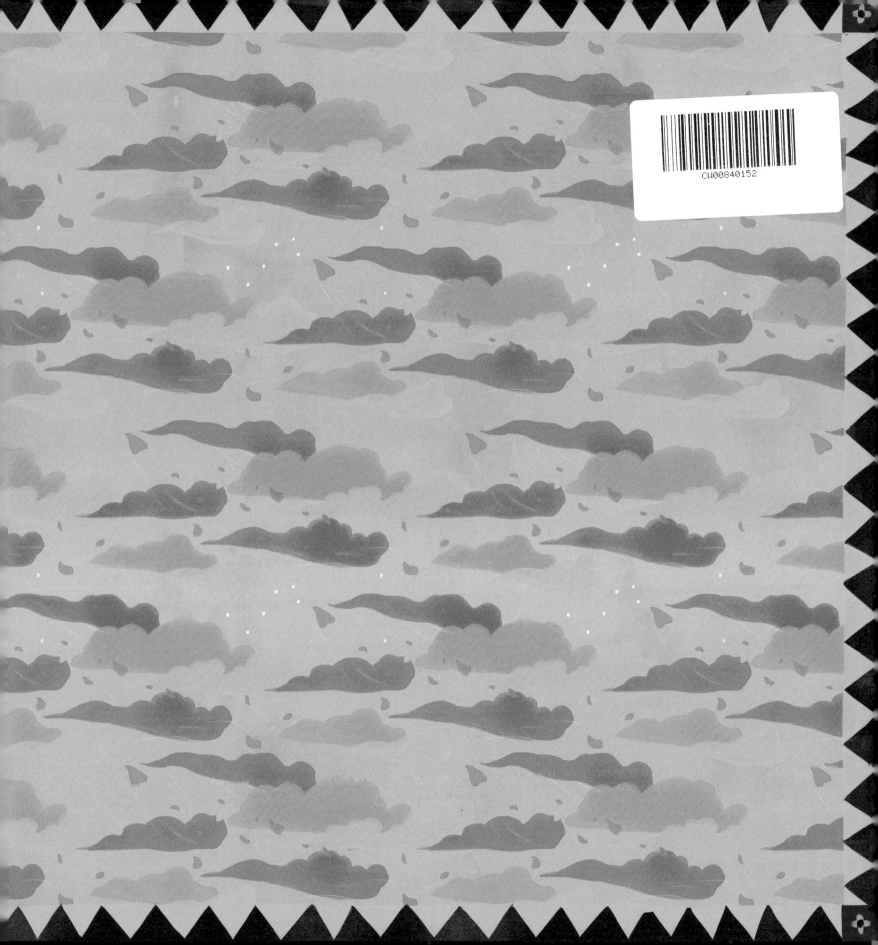

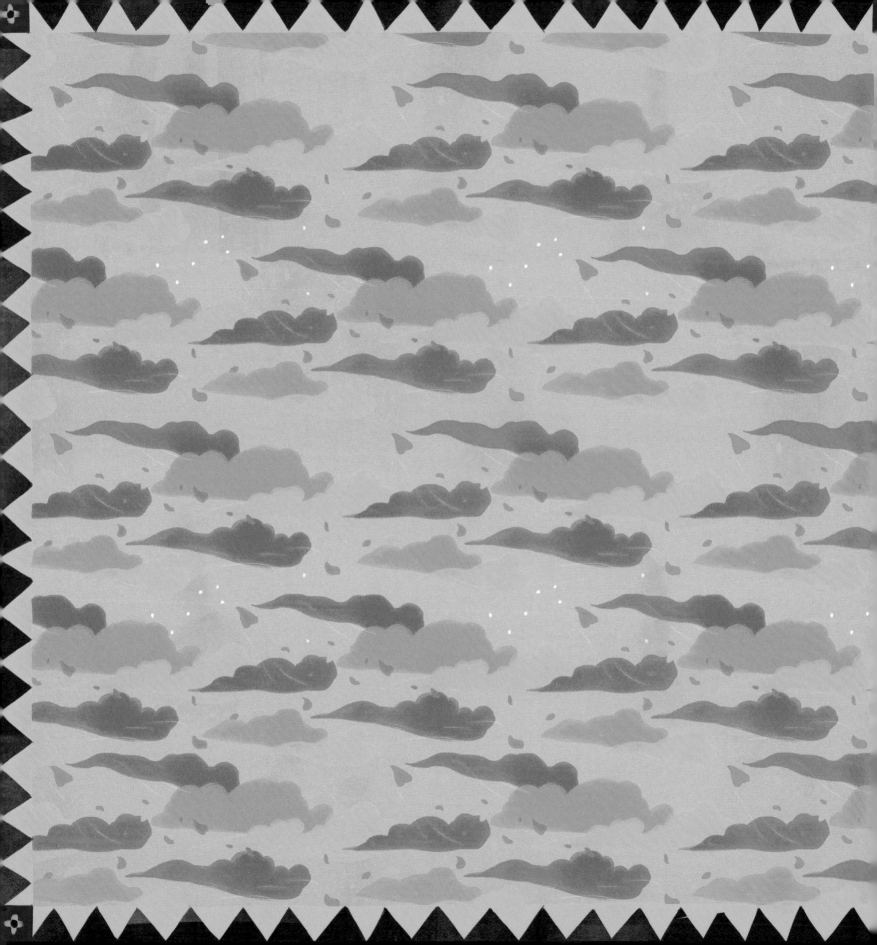

Blow, Wind, Blow!

Dom Conlon
Illustrations Anastasia Izlesou

This book belongs to:

_____

_____

_____

Blow, Wind, Blow!
Published in Great Britain in 2021 by Graffeg Limited.

Written by Dom Conlon copyright © 2021.
Illustrated by Anastasia Izlesou copyright © 2021.
Designed and produced by Graffeg copyright © 2021.

Graffeg, 24 Stradey Park Business Centre,
Mwrwg Road, Llangennech, Llanelli,
Carmarthenshire, SA14 8YP, Wales, UK.
Tel: 01554 824000. www.graffeg.com.

The publisher acknowledges the financial support
of the Books Council of Wales. www.gwales.com

ISBN 9781914079184

1 2 3 4 5 6 7 8 9

Blow, Wind, Blow!

Dom Conlon

Illustrations Anastasia Izlesou

GRAFFEG

Lawn-prowler, mist-parter,
like a cat on the hunt,
Wind watches clothes on a line.

But what can Wind do
– it's so small and weak –
what can it do to be strong?

Heat-snatcher, pressure-catcher,
Wind borrows strength from the Earth.

With a huff and a puff, Wind bellows a breeze
and the shirt sleeves all cheer in the air.

What a wheeze that was, what a blast of good fun,
now Wind wants to do it again.

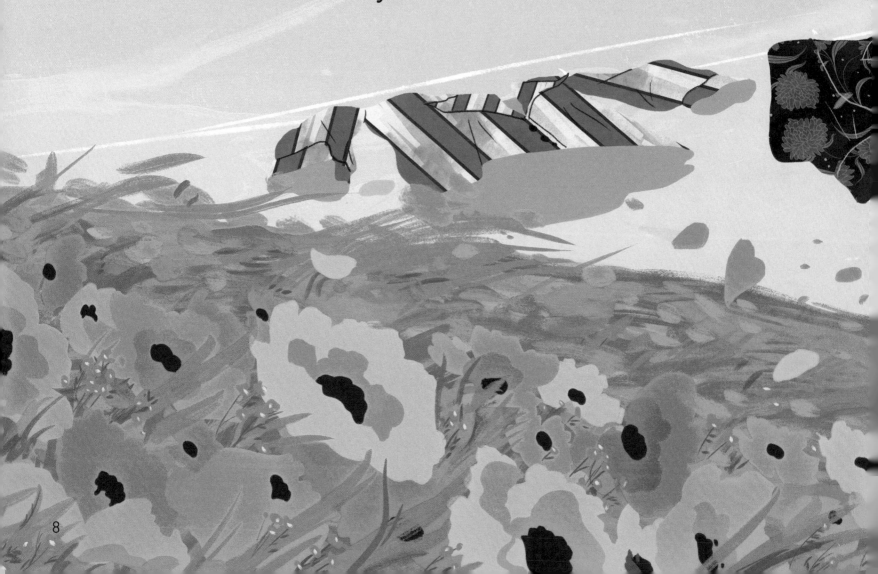

Go further, go farther
grow big and grow strong and
Blow, Wind, Blow!

9

ONE WAY

10

Curling over fences and into the trees
Wind scatters leaves like a sneeze.

And when a chirruping chick leaps from a nest,
Wind's breezy hands help her fly.

Then Wind plucks a sycamore seed from a tree
and helicopters it over the hills.

To Holland's stout windmills, which stand like white dresses,
grinding down grain for our cakes.

There's a flurry of flour – the miller's all white
and Wind whistles away with a laugh.

Go further, go farther
grow big and grow strong and
Blow, Wind, Blow!

13

Wind tickles the rivers then *whoosh*, on to Paris,
sending kites to write notes in the sky.

With a boost from a flame, Wind fills a balloon
like a puffed cheek ready to blow.

Two brothers clap hands, make a
breeze with a cheer,
and a sheep, duck and rooster lift off.

Now riding the trade winds far out to sea
Wind slows in the Pacific's doldrums.

Where it's still
where it's quiet
where the sea is like glass, so

go further, go farther
grow big and grow strong and
Blow, Wind, Blow!

Across Thailand and India, to Africa's deserts
to blow sandstorms through Chad and Sudan

whilst gazelles race along 'til they're quite out of breath
and a gale-force strength builds in Wind.

Go further, go farther
grow big and grow strong and

Blow, Wind, Blow!

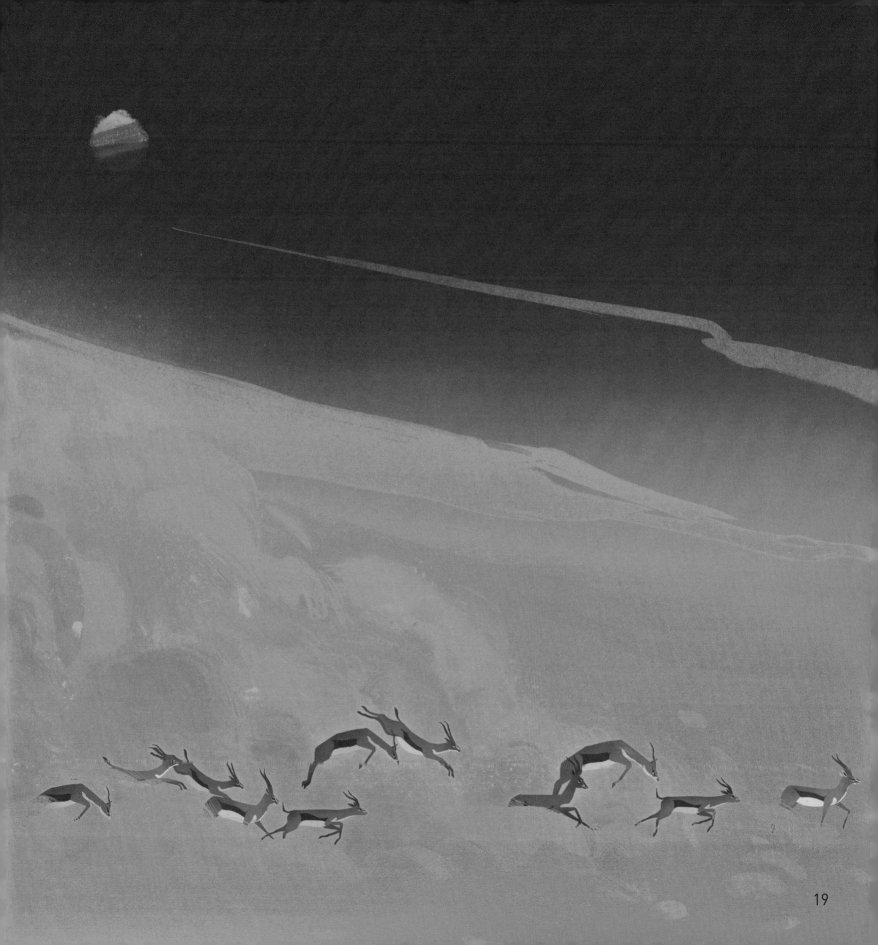

To the Atlantic's wild ocean with treasures of cloud
for pirate ships to fill up their sails.

Now the tropical waters are feeding Wind's thirst
and a hurricane's starting to form.

It's a cyclone, a typhoon, of water and wind
like a genie spinning out of control.

Go further, go farther
grow big and grow strong and

Blow, Wind, Blow!

Wind rushes to Florida, to the jetties and shores,
and the homes all lean back in surprise.

There are cars being flipped
as roofs peel away
and turbulence rattles the air.

22

Wind wants to have fun
but this isn't good so
Slow, Wind, Slow.

A blast of cold air from the Andes at last helps Wind to slowly calm down.

24

And somehow the seed still rides on its back
and now flutters and settles into Amazon soil
like a flag on a newly found moon.

Then creeping and peeping
Wind shuffles down streets
in search of somewhere to rest.

But doors all slam shut
and coats huddle up
and everyone says,

'Go, Wind, Go!'

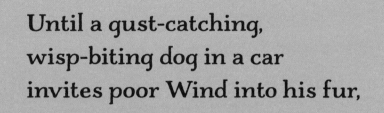

Until a gust-catching,
wisp-biting dog in a car
invites poor Wind into his fur,

And together they ripple and
soar along roads
shouting,

'Blow, Wind, BLOW!'

29

Wind Facts

Wind is what happens when air moves, and this is the story of the good things (and the bad things) it can do.

Some of the words and ideas in this book will be unfamiliar.

Balloon – Hot air rises. This was something discovered by the Montgolfier brothers and used to lift the very first balloon (which carried a duck, a sheep, and a rooster) in the year 1783.

Curl – Wind doesn't blow in a straight line, it curves. That's because the Earth rotates. This is called the Coriolis effect.

Doldrums – An area on the ocean with very little wind.

Heat-catcher/Pressure-snatcher – When the air gets warmer, its tiny molecules begin to move more quickly. If you watch a kettle boiling, you'll see the steam rise. As the air cools it, the steam will fall. When air moves it leaves behind an area of low pressure. More air rushes to fill that area – which we call WIND!

Hurricane – A powerful wind which starts over the water around the equator. It's also called a cyclone or typhoon depending on where it starts. A tornado is similar but starts on land.

Sycamore – The seeds of the sycamore tree spin like helicopter blades when they fall. A sycamore seed wouldn't really travel all the way to the Amazon Rainforest, but the wind does carry seeds to new places where they begin to grow.

Turbulence – Turbulence is rough air. It can happen for many reasons such as when winds collide or storms occur.

Trade winds – The name given to winds which sailors could rely on and use to sail by.

Windmills – Modern windmills generate electricity but older windmills used to grind grain into flour.

Dom Conlon

Dom Conlon is a double Carnegie-nominated poet and author whose work is guided by nature and the stars. He's written poetry and picture books, fact and fiction – sometimes all in the same book.

Nicola Davies said *Leap, Hare, Leap!* is 'full of the lushness of summer'. Chris Riddell said *This Rock That Rock* contained 'words and pictures that are quite simply out of this world'. Dallas Campbell said *Meet Matilda Rocket Builder* is 'a must read for all aspiring rocket scientists'.

Dom hopes to inspire everyone to read and write poetry. Discover more at www.domconlon.com.

Anastasia Izlesou

Anastasia Izlesou is an illustrator and graphic designer based in the UK.

Her work is full of bold natural elements and celebrates movement and shapes. Anastasia draws inspiration from her research and a wide variety of interests, which include the natural sciences, folklore and everyday objects.

Anastasia Izlesou was nominated for Kate Greenaway Medal for *Leap, Hare, Leap!*, published by Graffeg.

You can find more of her work at www.izlesou.co.uk.